P9-BYY-926

This Book belongs to

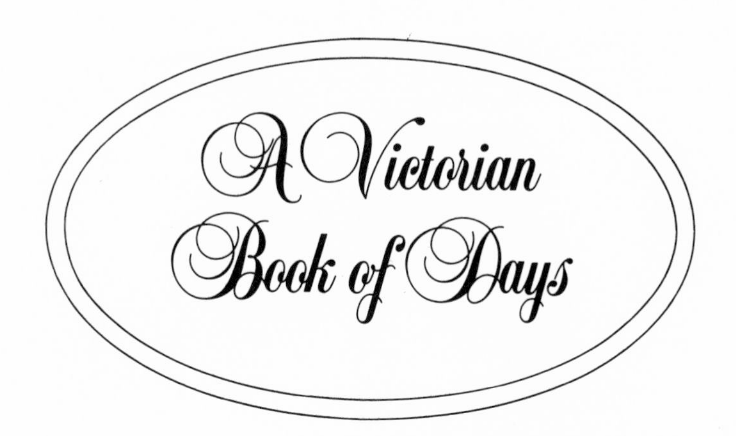
A Victorian
Book of Days

Published by The Ariel Press Ltd
1001 Hutchison House, Harcourt Road, Hong Kong

First published 1983
 ISBN 0 900074.337

Rose pattern based on an original design from the
Musèe des arts Decoratifs Paris

Printed in the United States of America

A Victorian Book of Days

By Avon

Introduction

T the center of the sumptuous, well-upholstered age we call Victorian is the diminutive figure of a Queen who set the tone of those expansive years between 1837 and 1901. She ruled an Empire on which the sun never set, but she was also a loving wife to her husband, Albert, and a caring and concerned, if regal, mother to their nine children. Queen Victoria took her responsibilities as ruler seriously, but the emotional center of her life and Albert's was their children and the family atmosphere of their houses on the Isle of Wight, in Scotland, and in the English countryside, not the social grandeur of London. Her subjects took their cue from the Royal family. The social scene in London, however, remained brilliant for four months of every year, led by Victoria's son Edward, Prince of Wales and his wife Alexandra, but even the beautiful Alexandra was described as "the dearest friend and constant companion" of her daughters. The handsome pictures in this diary, chosen from the period, give glimpses of this privileged, vanished world. Magnificently gowned and groomed ladies accompanied by deferential escorts move against a backdrop of ease and pleasure. Lady Margaret and her daughter, Constance, never existed outside these pages, but the life and attitudes depicted here were real, the distillation of the loves and lives of many women of the time. Such ease and graciousness will not come again.

January

Sunday 1

New Year's Day

Monday 2

Tuesday 3

Wednesday 4

Thursday 5

Friday 6

Epiphany

Saturday 7

January

Sunday 8

Monday 9

Tuesday 10

Wednesday 11

Thursday 12

Friday 13

Saturday 14

A Victorian Lady

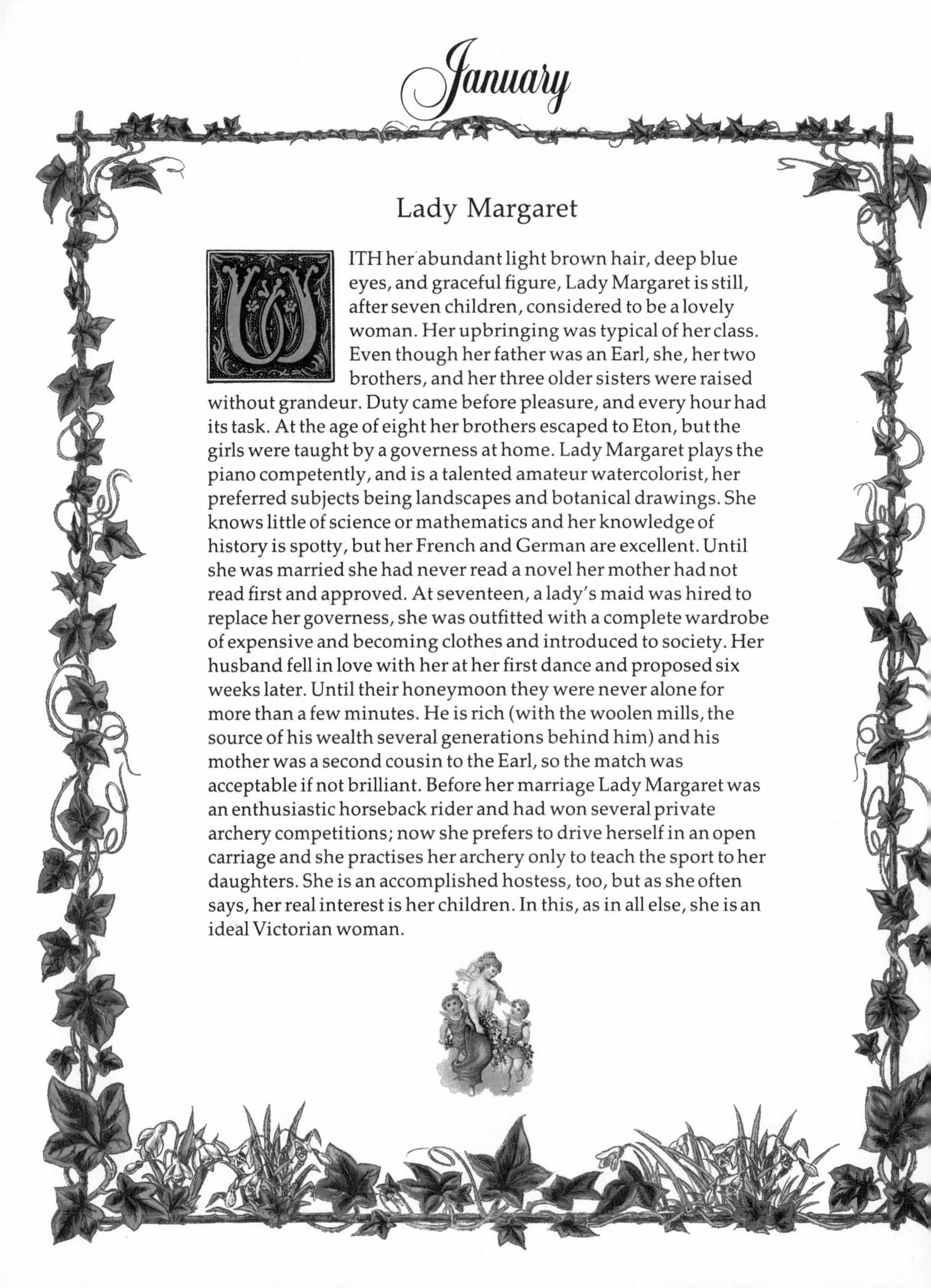

January

Lady Margaret

WITH her abundant light brown hair, deep blue eyes, and graceful figure, Lady Margaret is still, after seven children, considered to be a lovely woman. Her upbringing was typical of her class. Even though her father was an Earl, she, her two brothers, and her three older sisters were raised without grandeur. Duty came before pleasure, and every hour had its task. At the age of eight her brothers escaped to Eton, but the girls were taught by a governess at home. Lady Margaret plays the piano competently, and is a talented amateur watercolorist, her preferred subjects being landscapes and botanical drawings. She knows little of science or mathematics and her knowledge of history is spotty, but her French and German are excellent. Until she was married she had never read a novel her mother had not read first and approved. At seventeen, a lady's maid was hired to replace her governess, she was outfitted with a complete wardrobe of expensive and becoming clothes and introduced to society. Her husband fell in love with her at her first dance and proposed six weeks later. Until their honeymoon they were never alone for more than a few minutes. He is rich (with the woolen mills, the source of his wealth several generations behind him) and his mother was a second cousin to the Earl, so the match was acceptable if not brilliant. Before her marriage Lady Margaret was an enthusiastic horseback rider and had won several private archery competitions; now she prefers to drive herself in an open carriage and she practises her archery only to teach the sport to her daughters. She is an accomplished hostess, too, but as she often says, her real interest is her children. In this, as in all else, she is an ideal Victorian woman.

January

Sunday 15

Martin Luther King's Birthday

Monday 16

Tuesday 17

Wednesday 18

Thursday 19

Friday 20

Saturday 21

January

Sunday 22

Monday 23

Tuesday 24

Wednesday 25

Thursday 26

Friday 27

Saturday 28

Skating in the Park

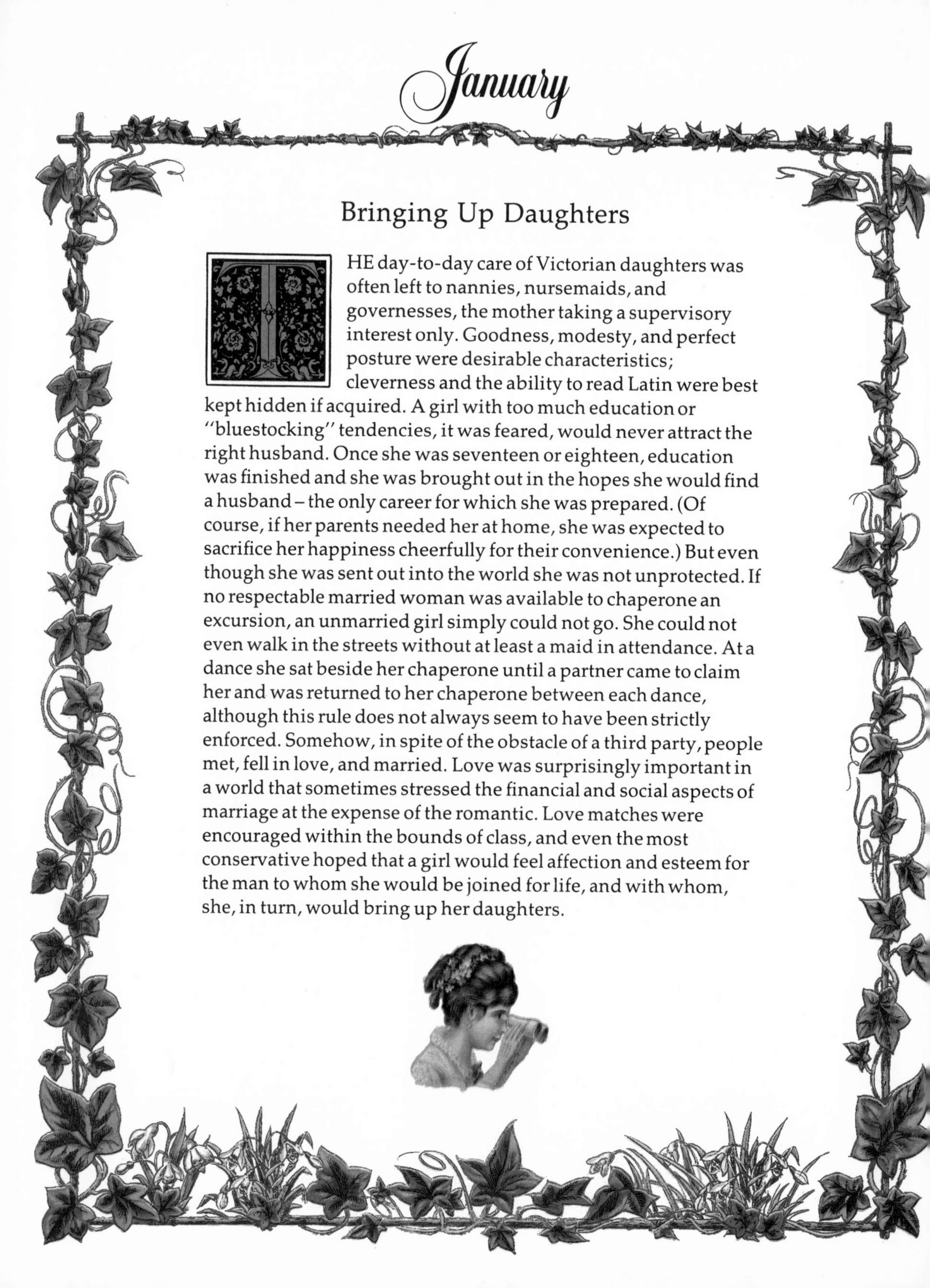

January

Bringing Up Daughters

THE day-to-day care of Victorian daughters was often left to nannies, nursemaids, and governesses, the mother taking a supervisory interest only. Goodness, modesty, and perfect posture were desirable characteristics; cleverness and the ability to read Latin were best kept hidden if acquired. A girl with too much education or "bluestocking" tendencies, it was feared, would never attract the right husband. Once she was seventeen or eighteen, education was finished and she was brought out in the hopes she would find a husband – the only career for which she was prepared. (Of course, if her parents needed her at home, she was expected to sacrifice her happiness cheerfully for their convenience.) But even though she was sent out into the world she was not unprotected. If no respectable married woman was available to chaperone an excursion, an unmarried girl simply could not go. She could not even walk in the streets without at least a maid in attendance. At a dance she sat beside her chaperone until a partner came to claim her and was returned to her chaperone between each dance, although this rule does not always seem to have been strictly enforced. Somehow, in spite of the obstacle of a third party, people met, fell in love, and married. Love was surprisingly important in a world that sometimes stressed the financial and social aspects of marriage at the expense of the romantic. Love matches were encouraged within the bounds of class, and even the most conservative hoped that a girl would feel affection and esteem for the man to whom she would be joined for life, and with whom, she, in turn, would bring up her daughters.

January-February

Sunday 29

Monday 30

Tuesday 31

Wednesday 1

Thursday 2

Ground Hog Day

Friday 3

Saturday 4

February

Sunday 5

Monday 6

Tuesday 7

Wednesday 8

Thursday 9

Friday 10

Saturday 11

Valentine's Day

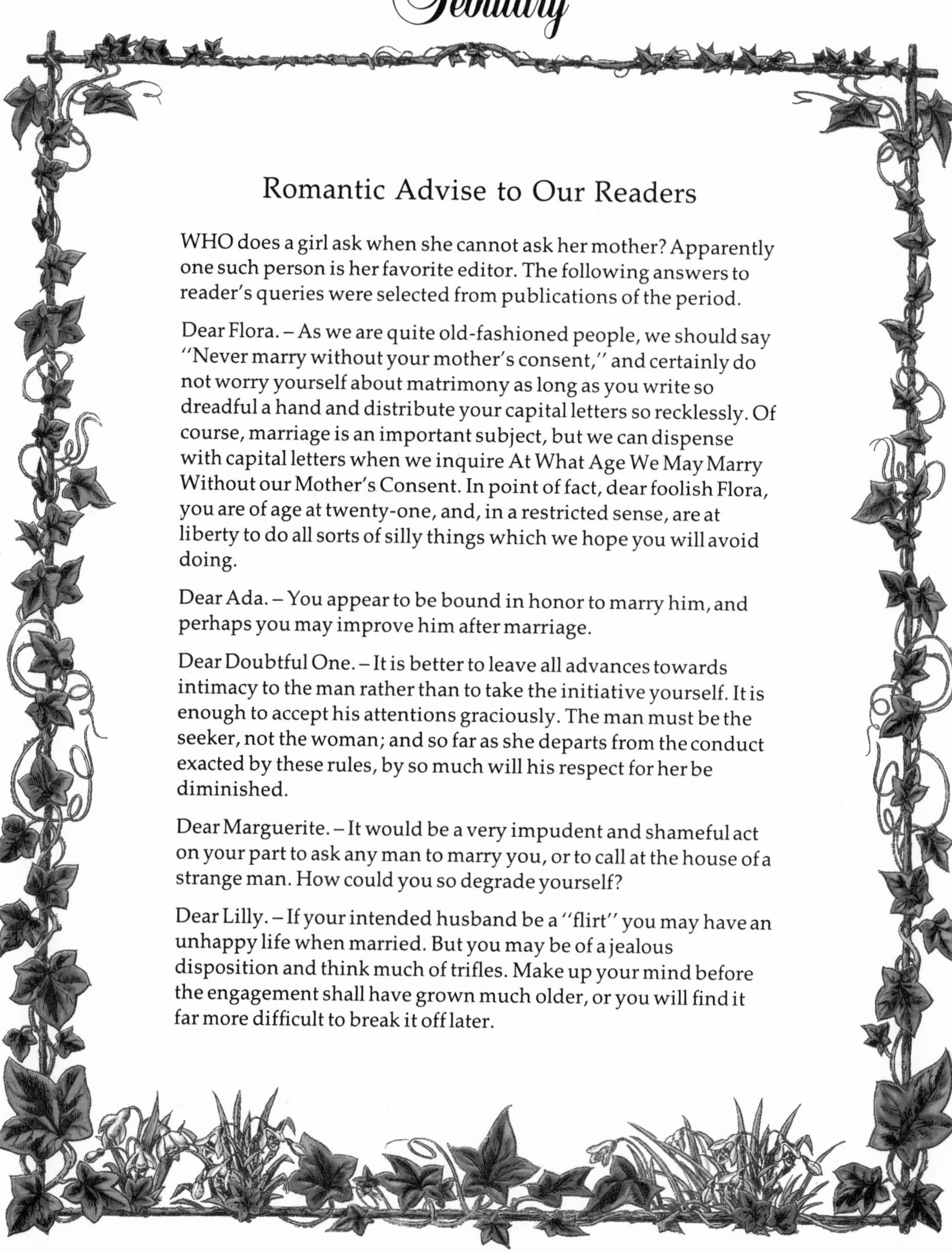

Romantic Advise to Our Readers

WHO does a girl ask when she cannot ask her mother? Apparently one such person is her favorite editor. The following answers to reader's queries were selected from publications of the period.

Dear Flora. – As we are quite old-fashioned people, we should say "Never marry without your mother's consent," and certainly do not worry yourself about matrimony as long as you write so dreadful a hand and distribute your capital letters so recklessly. Of course, marriage is an important subject, but we can dispense with capital letters when we inquire At What Age We May Marry Without our Mother's Consent. In point of fact, dear foolish Flora, you are of age at twenty-one, and, in a restricted sense, are at liberty to do all sorts of silly things which we hope you will avoid doing.

Dear Ada. – You appear to be bound in honor to marry him, and perhaps you may improve him after marriage.

Dear Doubtful One. – It is better to leave all advances towards intimacy to the man rather than to take the initiative yourself. It is enough to accept his attentions graciously. The man must be the seeker, not the woman; and so far as she departs from the conduct exacted by these rules, by so much will his respect for her be diminished.

Dear Marguerite. – It would be a very impudent and shameful act on your part to ask any man to marry you, or to call at the house of a strange man. How could you so degrade yourself?

Dear Lilly. – If your intended husband be a "flirt" you may have an unhappy life when married. But you may be of a jealous disposition and think much of trifles. Make up your mind before the engagement shall have grown much older, or you will find it far more difficult to break it off later.

February

Sunday 12

Lincoln's Birthday

Monday 13

Tuesday 14

St. Valentine's Day

Wednesday 15

Thursday 16

Friday 17

Saturday 18

February

Sunday 19

Monday 20

Washington's Birthday 'Observed'

Tuesday 21

Wednesday 22

Washington's Birthday

Thursday 23

Friday 24

Saturday 25

Following the Hunt

February

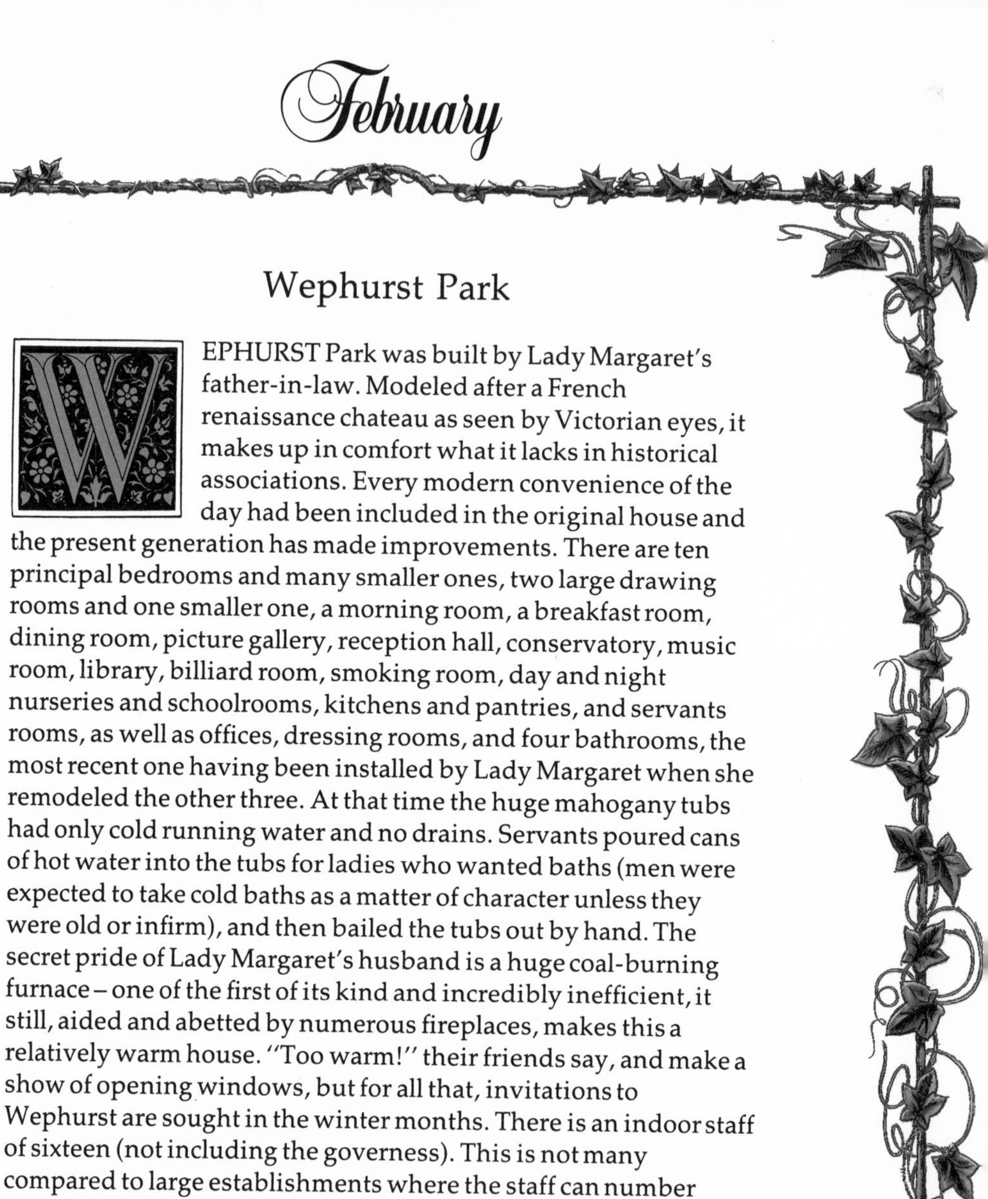

Wephurst Park

WEPHURST Park was built by Lady Margaret's father-in-law. Modeled after a French renaissance chateau as seen by Victorian eyes, it makes up in comfort what it lacks in historical associations. Every modern convenience of the day had been included in the original house and the present generation has made improvements. There are ten principal bedrooms and many smaller ones, two large drawing rooms and one smaller one, a morning room, a breakfast room, dining room, picture gallery, reception hall, conservatory, music room, library, billiard room, smoking room, day and night nurseries and schoolrooms, kitchens and pantries, and servants rooms, as well as offices, dressing rooms, and four bathrooms, the most recent one having been installed by Lady Margaret when she remodeled the other three. At that time the huge mahogany tubs had only cold running water and no drains. Servants poured cans of hot water into the tubs for ladies who wanted baths (men were expected to take cold baths as a matter of character unless they were old or infirm), and then bailed the tubs out by hand. The secret pride of Lady Margaret's husband is a huge coal-burning furnace – one of the first of its kind and incredibly inefficient, it still, aided and abetted by numerous fireplaces, makes this a relatively warm house. "Too warm!" their friends say, and make a show of opening windows, but for all that, invitations to Wephurst are sought in the winter months. There is an indoor staff of sixteen (not including the governess). This is not many compared to large establishments where the staff can number forty or more, but in a modern and convenient house it seems to be enough.

February-March

Sunday 26

Monday 27

Tuesday 28

Wednesday 29

Thursday 1

Friday 2

Saturday 3

March

Sunday 4

Monday 5

Tuesday 6

Wednesday 7

Ash Wednesday

Thursday 8

Friday 9

Saturday 10

The Letter

A Weekend in the Country

ISITS used to mean weeks or even months, but with the expansion of the railway to every village and town, busy people can come up from London on Friday or Saturday for the weekend, sometimes joining a house party in progress. Lady Margaret and her husband often have from six to twelve visitors. Stiff white cards on each bedroom door indicate, in copperplate handwriting, the intended occupant. Guests arrive with a good deal of luggage since everyone changes clothes several times a day and dresses for dinner, even in the country. Ladies bring their maids if they have them, and most do. It is almost impossible for fashionable women to dress themselves and arrange their hair without assistance. One of the Wephurst servants unpacks for those who have no help, cleans their boots and shoes, and brushes their clothes. Guests ring for tea when they wake and hot water is brought by the footmen and upstairs maids in big, steaming cans (guests have washstands in their rooms and may have a bath there, if they prefer it, in a tub in front of the fire). Breakfast is between 8 a.m. and noon – guests serve themselves from a generous sideboard. Horses are provided and, in season, men may shoot or hunt. Ladies sometimes hunt or go for walks in the grounds. After lunch, in fine weather, Lady Margaret likes to organize a croquet match, lawn tennis, or an excursion into the village. Tea is at 4:30. At 7:30 the gong warns those who have not changed that dinner will be served in half an hour. After dinner they may have an informal dance or even an evening of charades and games. There are tables for bridge and backgammon and a fine library. On Monday morning the weekenders go back to town, leaving the rest of the house party guests to continue their country pursuits.

March

Sunday 11

Monday 12

Tuesday 13

Wednesday 14

Thursday 15

Friday 16

Saturday 17

St. Patrick's Day

March

Sunday 18

Monday 19

Tuesday 20

Wednesday 21

Thursday 22

Friday 23

Saturday 24

The Competition

Charles Frederick Worth 1825-1895

HARLES Frederick Worth ruled the world of fashion with the same confidence with which Victoria ruled the Empire. English by birth, he left London when he was twenty to work in Paris, the center of women's fashion even then. He met his wife while they both worked in a shop. Her innate elegance was his inspiration, and her person was his first and best model. Dressed in the clothes he designed and made for her, she attracted the attention of the fashionable world, and soon Worth was in partnership with his former employer. By 1857 he had his own elegant store, and a clientele so exclusive that an introduction was needed before he would sell a customer a dress. He made many innovations in the selling of clothes as well as the designing of them, and his fame was helped as much by his genius at self-promotion as his genius as a designer. He was the first to show a whole collection to customers at the beginning of the season and the first to use live models. He disliked the crinoline, although he designed many, and gradually he encouraged the new silhouette that became the bustle. On special occasions his best customers dressed at his shop, going directly from there to a party or ball, having first had every detail of their appearance overseen by Worth. At the height of his fame and popularity it is reported that he received customers while reclining on a sofa, ordering them to walk and turn, and telling them to come back in a week, when he would have a *toilette* for them. The customer no longer chose; Worth's choice was the one that mattered.

March

Sunday 25

Monday 26

Tuesday 27

Wednesday 28

Thursday 29

Friday 30

Saturday 31

April

Sunday 1

April Fool's Day

Monday 2

Tuesday 3

Wednesday 4

Thursday 5

Friday 6

Saturday 7

Paying a Call

The Season

PRIL, May, June, and July are the four months that comprise that giddy social whirl called the London Season. For at least part of these months every year – except when she is visibly pregnant – Lady Margaret and her husband open their house in Belgravia and go to town to entertain and to be entertained. Queen Victoria has been living a retired life since Albert died in 1861 and her place in society has been filled by her son Edward, Prince of Wales, and his beautiful and much admired wife, Princess Alexandra. This year Constance, Lady Margaret's oldest daughter, will be presented at court and so the family is going to London for the whole Season (except for Gerald the oldest son who is at Oxford and will come down for the weekends). Constance is a very pretty girl, and her family has every hope of getting her comfortably matched, which is, after all, the real point of the Season. To that end her mother, grandmother, and aunts will chaperone her and accompany her to cinderella balls, which are strictly for other young people and end promptly at midnight; to large balls where all ages of society mix; to drums, soirées and crushes which are large parties with no dancing; to breakfasts that begin at 3 p.m. and to dinners that begin at 8 p.m. to picnics and garden parties; to race meetings, regattas, and cricket matches; to the opera and "musical evenings." And at some time during those busy four months it is hoped that Constance will meet her future husband. Then the Season will have been a success.

April

Sunday 8

Monday 9

Tuesday 10

Wednesday 11

Thursday 12

Friday 13

Saturday 14

April

Sunday 15

Palm Sunday

Monday 16

Tuesday 17

Passover

Wednesday 18

Thursday 19

Friday 20

Good Friday

Saturday 21

The Easter Parade

Etiquette

THE young, the socially insecure, and those trying to make their way in society also sought the editor's advice. Below are some answers on matters of etiquette from periodicals of the time.

Inez. – When you pay a visit, give your name very distinctly to the servant who opens the door, but do not send in a card. Only strangers calling for the purpose of collecting for charities, or on business, need send in a card.

Peggy. – Girls of fifteen are not "in society" (if belonging to the upper classes), and if they appear after a home dinner, or when visitors call at the house, they should be retiring and not enter into general conversation, but speak when spoken to by strangers. Then do so freely and modestly.

One in doubt. – A guest or visitor should always be addressed before greeting any of your own family; it would be impolite to salute your wife or daughter before speaking to the visitor, unless you were calling at a house other than your own, and then the lady of the house or her daughter, receiving in her place, must be addressed before anyone else.

Nora. – Leave one card of your own, and two for your husband, if not admitted. If you go in, leave your husband's (two) on the hall table, when you go. Should there be daughters already in society, leave a second card (your own) for them; and if you chance to have but one left, turn up one side to show you meant the one card for all. The initials P.P.C. are those of three French words *Pour prendre conge*, literally rendered, "for to take leave." Sometimes the farewell is otherwise expressed by P.D.A. – *Pour des adieux*, and in English T.T.O. – to take leave.

Wishing to be Polite. – Only bow and look pleasant when a gentleman is introduced to you. (You should not be introduced to a man.)

April

Sunday 22

Easter Sunday

Monday 23

Tuesday 24

Wednesday 25

Thursday 26

Friday 27

Saturday 28

April-May

Sunday 29

Monday 30

Tuesday 1

Wednesday 2

Thursday 3

Friday 4

Saturday 5

The Regatta

May

A Wardrobe

LADY Margaret has always dressed her daughter, Constance, in simply made schoolgirl outfits of wool or linen. Now that she is eighteen, a new wardrobe is to be chosen to show her off to best advantage: tailor-made dresses for walking in fawn covert coating with a reverse side of heliotrope and a heather tweed mixture; morning dresses of soft lemon yellow, green and apricot; tennis or boating dresses in blue and biscuit linen, edged with braid; skirts of golden brown, slate gray, and bottle green to be worn with jackets fitted to the waist and dainty muslin blouses with puffed sleeves and ruffled yokes. All these are entrusted to a London dressmaker. For more complicated *toilettes* there is a trip to Paris. Constance dresses less elaborately than her mother as becomes a young girl, but she will need at least ten evening dresses, including one of pale blue silk with festoons of silk caught up with rosettes of ribbon, another of cream *mousseline de soie* with red-currant colored velvet ribbons, and a dress for smaller dinner parties or cinderella balls of gray and white glacé check. For lawn parties, white Indian muslin will suffice; for Ascot, a petunia-cloth striped dress with a fragile silk bow; for morning calls and promenading in Hyde Park, figured silk afternoon dresses and a crepôn dress of her favorite rose pink trimmed with a chiffon frill. Hats or bonnets for each outfit as well as mantles, parasols, stockings, boots, frothy embroidered and lace-edged petticoats, and two dozen pairs of gloves complete her wardrobe. Her French maid has been trained to dress her hair in the latest and most becoming styles. Her look is shy but confident. Constance is ready to make her entry into society.

May

Sunday 6

Monday 7

Tuesday 8

Wednesday 9

Thursday 10

Friday 11

Saturday 12

May

Sunday 13

Mother's Day

Monday 14

Tuesday 15

Wednesday 16

Thursday 17

Friday 18

Saturday 19

Debutantes at The Palace

May

Presentation at the Palace

GIRLS are presented at court in a Drawing Room when they come out and again after they are married. Like other debutantes, Constance is taking special classes to learn how to manage the unaccustomed long train of her court dress gracefully. On the day, she will dress in the white silk and chiffon dress specially made for this occasion – all debutantes wear white to be presented, just as they all carry large bouquets, wear court trains, veils, and two little curled ostrich plumes in their headdress (married women wear three.) Then Constance and her mother, who is sponsoring her, go to a photographer to have an official portrait taken. On to Buckingham Palace! A throng of people is gathered outside to peer into the carriages as they approach in a slow line with their nervous passengers. Inside the palace it is very crowded with girls and their sponsors. Trains are neatly folded in three and laid over arms to keep them from being trampled in the crush. When it is Constance's turn the pages arrange her train and veil, and her pink card is given to the Lord-in-Waiting who calls out the names of the girl and her sponsor. Since the Queen herself is present Constance curtsies deeply and kisses the air two inches above the royal hand (the Queen does not like to have her hand actually touched), then curtsies to each of the other Royals present, after which she backs gracefully from the room in the gliding crab-like steps she has been taught – without tripping over her train or turning her back on any of the Royalty present. Constance is officially "out" in society.

May

Sunday 20

Monday 21

Tuesday 22

Wednesday 23

Thursday 24

Friday 25

Saturday 26

May-June

Sunday 27

Monday 28

Tuesday 29

Wednesday 30

Memorial Day

Thursday 31

Friday 1

Saturday 2

Derby Day

June

Ah, Fashion!

NOTHING looks so ridiculous as the fashionable follies of an earlier generation. Like most of us, the Victorians were aware of fashions' foibles. They saw them clearly in the previous generation and resolutely ignored sensible advice in their own for the sake of beauty. Not that in the sixty years of Victoria's reign fashions did not undergo a number of changes. The bell-shaped crinolines with their multitude of petticoats yielded to the swaying cages of the hoop skirts which, in turn, were gradually flattened and pulled toward the back of the dress as they evolved into the bustle that dominated fashion until almost the end of the century. If the width of crinolines had made travel in coaches, carriages, and hansom cabs difficult, walking in a high wind embarrassing, and taking the arm of a gentleman impossible, then the bustled mode could be seen as an improvement. Of course, sitting down in an ordinary chair with a foot or two of steel or horsehair draped with fabric protruding behind might be uncomfortable, long trains that dragged three feet on the ground could pick up every kind of unaesthetic litter, and skirts on afternoon dresses grew so tight that steps were confined to an unsteady totter, but what of that? There are few discomforts that cannot be born with the help of the comfortable glow of assurance that pervades us when we know we look "right." And that feeling is the one constant in fashion from Victoria's time to our own.

June

Sunday 3

Monday 4

Tuesday 5

Wednesday 6

Thursday 7

Friday 8

Saturday 9

June

Sunday 10

Monday 11

Tuesday 12

Wednesday 13

Thursday 14

Friday 15

Saturday 16

Royal Ascot

Victorian "Don'ts"

Don't adopt the latest mode.
Don't trail your dress upon the road.
Don't ever lace your waist too tightly.
Don't wear a glove or boot unsightly.
Don't wear a thing that needs repair.
Don't, please, forget to brush your hair.
Don't ever wear too large a check.
Don't show too much of snowy neck.
Don't paint the lilies and roses on your face, fair maiden.
Don't have windows in your gloves and stockings, where they were never intended to be.
Don't think the love your tiny waist wins will wash; because it won't.
Don't think because your neighbor's bonnet is becoming to her, it will necessarily be becoming to yourself.
Don't go in for quantity so much as quality in dress. One well-made gown is worth half a dozen ill-fitting ones.
Don't neglect the accessories of dress; untidy gloves, unshapely shoes, will destroy the effect of the most charming *toilette*.
Don't, above all things, forget you are a woman; she is far more attractive when seen in the flowing draperies that centuries of use have made their own, than when masquerading as a man.
Don't buy hats at the expense of boots.
Don't buy in haste and repent at leisure.
Don't ignore the conventional, and torture your friends with "a style of my own."
Don't wear dead rats round your throat, though it be the fashion.
Don't neglect the neat tying of a veil.
Don't put your gloves on in the street.

Advice to women in the 1890s

June

Sunday 17

Father's Day

Monday 18

Tuesday 19

Wednesday 20

Thursday 21

Friday 22

Saturday 23

June

Sunday 24

Monday 25

Tuesday 26

Wednesday 27

Thursday 28

Friday 29

Saturday 30

Her Escorts

The Ball

URING the Season, dances and balls of all sizes were given almost every night but Saturday and Sunday. The most exciting were the grand balls such as the ones given twice a year by the Prince and Princess of Wales and some of the other possessors of houses with large ballrooms. At these great events, all ages and ranks of the Upper Ten Thousand mixed, and it was here that a successful young debutante might hope to be introduced to an appropriate older man who was of her class if not her set. Married women had their own circle of respectful admirers, and often could be seen to be as much a belle as their younger, unmarried daughters. Men not actively searching for a wife often preferred the older woman's knowledge of the world to the younger one's still-shy schoolroom manners. Balls were not given as frequently in the country, but masquerades, hunt balls, squire's balls and others gave those who loved dancing, opportunities to keep their steps polished. The four most popular dances were the Quadrille, the Lancer's, the polka, and the waltz. The Quadrille and the Lancer's were both square dances with a series of complicated steps that the dancers memorized. The polka was energetic and in polite society the dancers were to be spirited but not boisterous. The waltz was the new Viennese waltz, considered to be much superior to the German kind. Victoria kept Albert up late dancing it; the guests at the Duke of Marlborough's coming-of-age party danced it until dawn; and Jennie Jerome Churchill went into premature labor with her son Winston, the future prime minister, while waltzing at Blenheim Palace. To keep the dancers refreshed a light (by Victorian standards) midnight supper was served – champagne, oyster patties, lobster and chicken salad, cakes, jellies, ices, shrimps, meringues, tongue, and small hams – after which the dancing continued until 3:00 or 4:00 in the morning.

July

Sunday 1

Monday 2

Tuesday 3

Wednesday 4

Independence Day

Thursday 5

Friday 6

Saturday 7

July

Sunday 8

Monday 9

Tuesday 10

Wednesday 11

Thursday 12

Friday 13

Saturday 14

Hyde Park on a Sunday

July

A Day in Town

LADY Margaret rises at 8 a.m. when she is in London. She has breakfast, reads and answers her mail, then tells her maid her plans and clothes for the day. After that she bathes and dresses and at 9:30 a.m. spends a half hour with the young children. At 10 a.m. she meets with the butler and then the housekeeper to discuss the details of the household. She changes from her morning dress to a walking dress and her open carriage is brought around. She and Constance go for a fitting at the dressmaker, then for a drive in Rotten Row, that part of Hyde Park which is reserved for "society" to ride, drive and stroll through between 11 a.m. and 2 p.m. They then go home and change into afternoon dresses and are off to a luncheon. After lunch Lady Margaret, who is very punctilious in these matters, pays three morning calls (formal calls which can be made until 4 p.m. in the afternoon and which last 15 or 20 minutes each), two of them on hostesses who entertained them the day before. Tea time at 5 p.m. finds her dressed in a soft tea gown, and several friends of hers and Margaret's stop by for informal visits. After tea she changes for dinner, the opera or the theater and goes up to say goodnight to the children before going out. Although dinners often have as many as twelve courses, people are expected to go on to other parties or balls afterward – the host and hostess included. At 2 or 3 a.m. in the morning Lady Margaret tumbles into bed for a well-earned rest before starting the next day's round of pleasures.

July

Sunday 15

Monday 16

Tuesday 17

Wednesday 18

Thursday 19

Friday 20

Saturday 21

July

Sunday 22

Monday 23

Tuesday 24

Wednesday 25

Thursday 26

Friday 27

Saturday 28

The Lady Cyclists

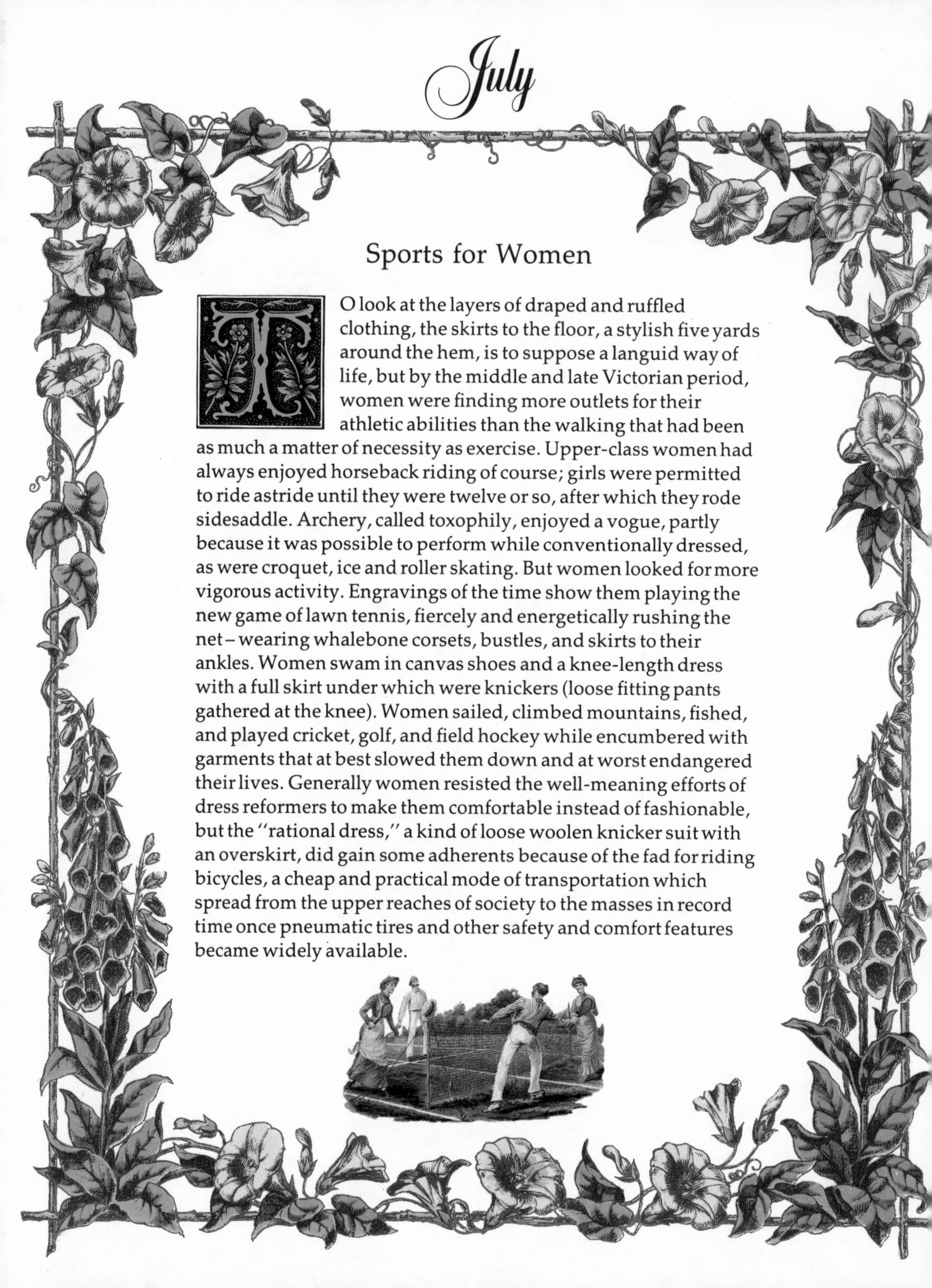

July

Sports for Women

TO look at the layers of draped and ruffled clothing, the skirts to the floor, a stylish five yards around the hem, is to suppose a languid way of life, but by the middle and late Victorian period, women were finding more outlets for their athletic abilities than the walking that had been as much a matter of necessity as exercise. Upper-class women had always enjoyed horseback riding of course; girls were permitted to ride astride until they were twelve or so, after which they rode sidesaddle. Archery, called toxophily, enjoyed a vogue, partly because it was possible to perform while conventionally dressed, as were croquet, ice and roller skating. But women looked for more vigorous activity. Engravings of the time show them playing the new game of lawn tennis, fiercely and energetically rushing the net – wearing whalebone corsets, bustles, and skirts to their ankles. Women swam in canvas shoes and a knee-length dress with a full skirt under which were knickers (loose fitting pants gathered at the knee). Women sailed, climbed mountains, fished, and played cricket, golf, and field hockey while encumbered with garments that at best slowed them down and at worst endangered their lives. Generally women resisted the well-meaning efforts of dress reformers to make them comfortable instead of fashionable, but the "rational dress," a kind of loose woolen knicker suit with an overskirt, did gain some adherents because of the fad for riding bicycles, a cheap and practical mode of transportation which spread from the upper reaches of society to the masses in record time once pneumatic tires and other safety and comfort features became widely available.

July-August

Sunday 29

Monday 30

Tuesday 31

Wednesday 1

Thursday 2

Friday 3

Saturday 4

August

Sunday 5

Monday 6

Tuesday 7

Wednesday 8

Thursday 9

Friday 10

Saturday 11

By the Sea

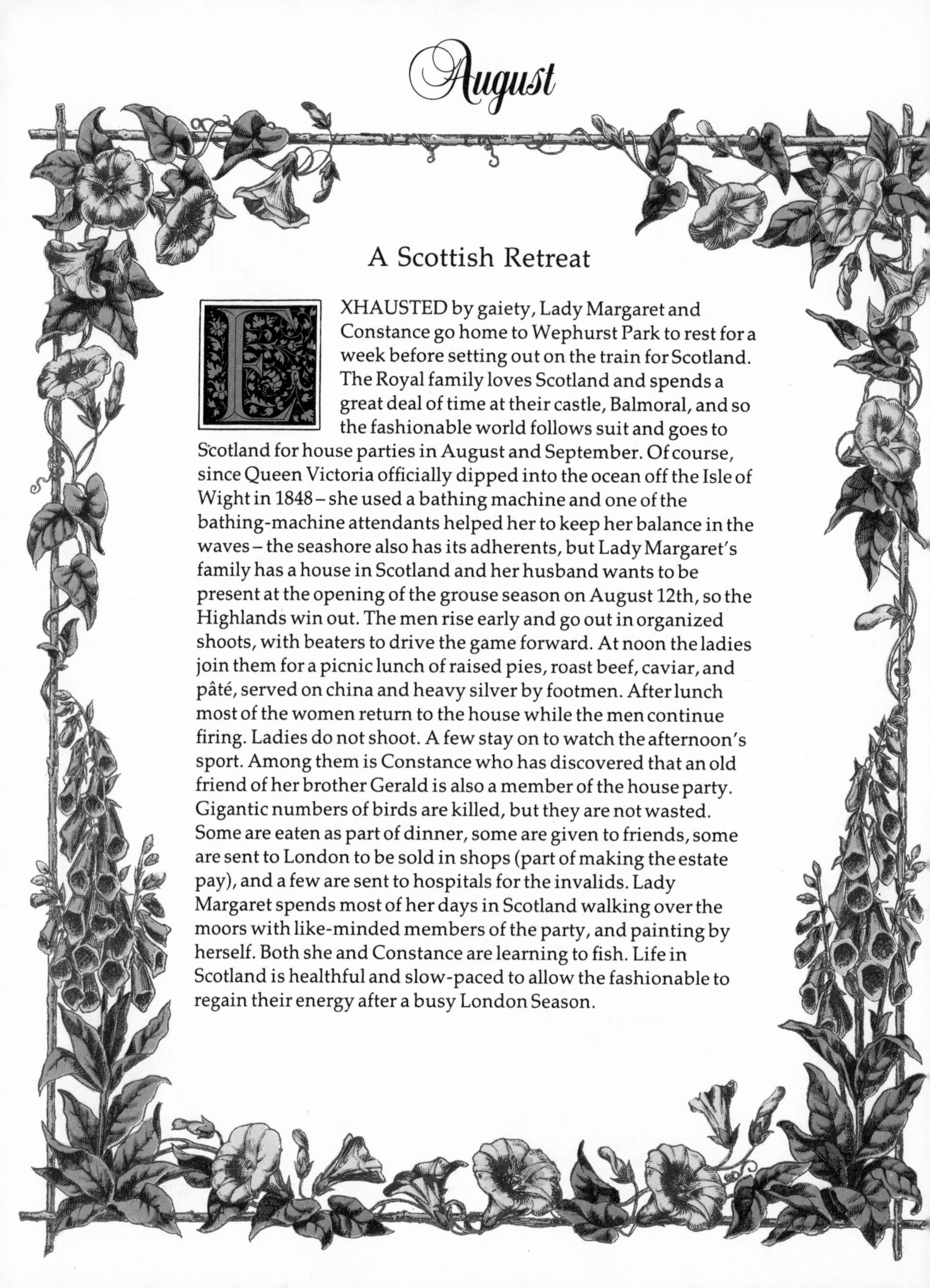

August

A Scottish Retreat

EXHAUSTED by gaiety, Lady Margaret and Constance go home to Wephurst Park to rest for a week before setting out on the train for Scotland. The Royal family loves Scotland and spends a great deal of time at their castle, Balmoral, and so the fashionable world follows suit and goes to Scotland for house parties in August and September. Of course, since Queen Victoria officially dipped into the ocean off the Isle of Wight in 1848 – she used a bathing machine and one of the bathing-machine attendants helped her to keep her balance in the waves – the seashore also has its adherents, but Lady Margaret's family has a house in Scotland and her husband wants to be present at the opening of the grouse season on August 12th, so the Highlands win out. The men rise early and go out in organized shoots, with beaters to drive the game forward. At noon the ladies join them for a picnic lunch of raised pies, roast beef, caviar, and pâté, served on china and heavy silver by footmen. After lunch most of the women return to the house while the men continue firing. Ladies do not shoot. A few stay on to watch the afternoon's sport. Among them is Constance who has discovered that an old friend of her brother Gerald is also a member of the house party. Gigantic numbers of birds are killed, but they are not wasted. Some are eaten as part of dinner, some are given to friends, some are sent to London to be sold in shops (part of making the estate pay), and a few are sent to hospitals for the invalids. Lady Margaret spends most of her days in Scotland walking over the moors with like-minded members of the party, and painting by herself. Both she and Constance are learning to fish. Life in Scotland is healthful and slow-paced to allow the fashionable to regain their energy after a busy London Season.

August

Sunday 12

Monday 13

Tuesday 14

Wednesday 15

Thursday 16

Friday 17

Saturday 18

August

Sunday 19

Monday 20

Tuesday 21

Wednesday 22

Thursday 23

Friday 24

Saturday 25

At the River

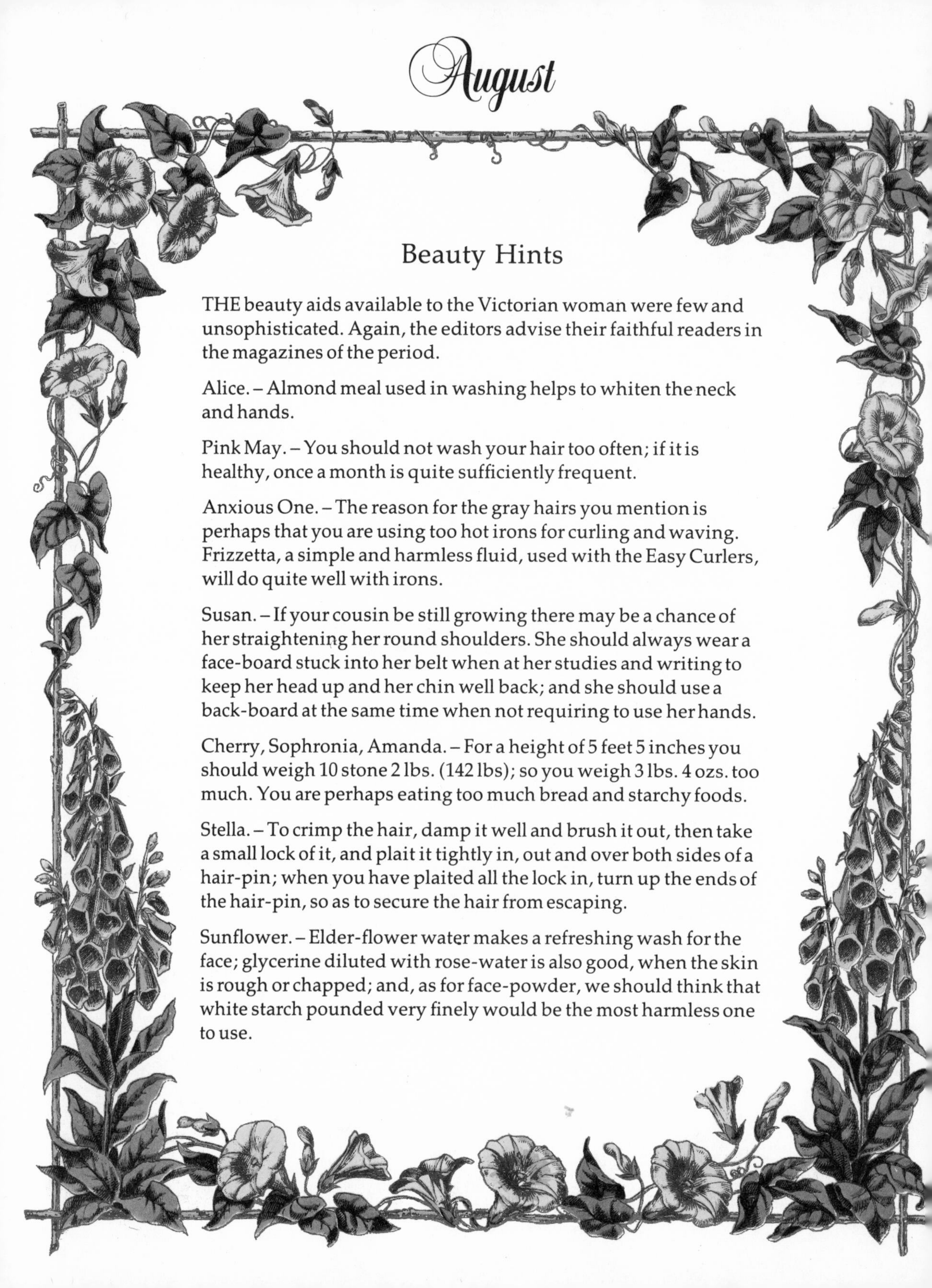

August

Beauty Hints

THE beauty aids available to the Victorian woman were few and unsophisticated. Again, the editors advise their faithful readers in the magazines of the period.

Alice. – Almond meal used in washing helps to whiten the neck and hands.

Pink May. – You should not wash your hair too often; if it is healthy, once a month is quite sufficiently frequent.

Anxious One. – The reason for the gray hairs you mention is perhaps that you are using too hot irons for curling and waving. Frizzetta, a simple and harmless fluid, used with the Easy Curlers, will do quite well with irons.

Susan. – If your cousin be still growing there may be a chance of her straightening her round shoulders. She should always wear a face-board stuck into her belt when at her studies and writing to keep her head up and her chin well back; and she should use a back-board at the same time when not requiring to use her hands.

Cherry, Sophronia, Amanda. – For a height of 5 feet 5 inches you should weigh 10 stone 2 lbs. (142 lbs); so you weigh 3 lbs. 4 ozs. too much. You are perhaps eating too much bread and starchy foods.

Stella. – To crimp the hair, damp it well and brush it out, then take a small lock of it, and plait it tightly in, out and over both sides of a hair-pin; when you have plaited all the lock in, turn up the ends of the hair-pin, so as to secure the hair from escaping.

Sunflower. – Elder-flower water makes a refreshing wash for the face; glycerine diluted with rose-water is also good, when the skin is rough or chapped; and, as for face-powder, we should think that white starch pounded very finely would be the most harmless one to use.

August-September

Sunday 26

Monday 27

Tuesday 28

Wednesday 29

Thursday 30

Friday 31

Saturday 1

September

Sunday 2

Monday 3

Labor Day

Tuesday 4

Wednesday 5

Thursday 6

Friday 7

Saturday 8

A Sketch from Nature

September

Fashion Notes

STAYING in fashion at a time when communications were relatively slow between town and country, keeping clothes fresh when dry cleaning was an infant industry and flat-irons had to be heated on the stove, and figuring out a hair style which you had only read about and never seen, were problems of great interest to women who lived any distance from the metropolitan centers. Again, the editors offer the following comments and advice in periodicals of the time.

"In the country most people wear a jacket and skirt of tweed, serge or homespun, with a pretty blouse or front, all day; but in other cases, as in London, the morning dress would be changed after lunch."

"We must not forget to mention a novelty, the advantages of which will be readily understood by all persons who know how beneficial flannel is to health. The novelty consists of flannel stays, made in striped material, red and black, black and white, and many other mixtures of colors."

"Young unmarried ladies are following the example of their seniors, and adorning their heads with winged insects. Many butterflies are made in Paris of pearls, with diamond eyes. These are to be worn alighting at the top of a coronet, and a white rose low on the neck at the back."

"Velvet may be cleaned by rubbing lightly with bacon rind; but if of a very good quality, it would be better to send it to a professional cleaner."

"Yes, it is quite true that a woman's dress has been woven from spider's webs. Our own Queen (Victoria) is in possession of it, having received it as a present from the late Empress of Brazil in 1877. It is said that it surpasses the most costly silk in both delicacy of fiber and beauty."

September

Sunday 9

Monday 10

Tuesday 11

Wednesday 12

Thursday 13

Friday 14

Saturday 15

September

Sunday 16

Monday 17

Tuesday 18

Wednesday 19

Thursday 20

Friday 21

Saturday 22

The Village Market

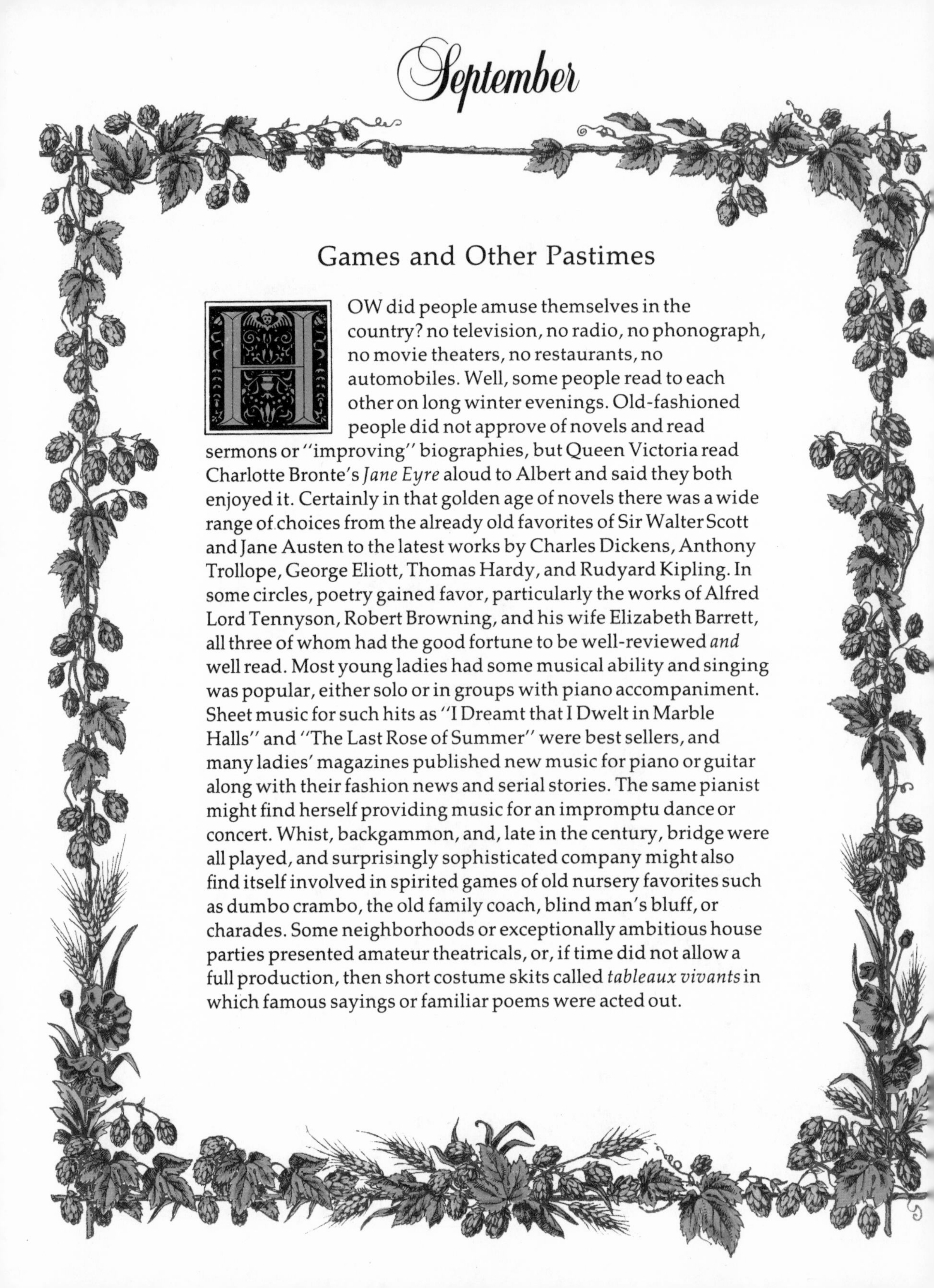

September

Games and Other Pastimes

HOW did people amuse themselves in the country? no television, no radio, no phonograph, no movie theaters, no restaurants, no automobiles. Well, some people read to each other on long winter evenings. Old-fashioned people did not approve of novels and read sermons or "improving" biographies, but Queen Victoria read Charlotte Bronte's *Jane Eyre* aloud to Albert and said they both enjoyed it. Certainly in that golden age of novels there was a wide range of choices from the already old favorites of Sir Walter Scott and Jane Austen to the latest works by Charles Dickens, Anthony Trollope, George Eliott, Thomas Hardy, and Rudyard Kipling. In some circles, poetry gained favor, particularly the works of Alfred Lord Tennyson, Robert Browning, and his wife Elizabeth Barrett, all three of whom had the good fortune to be well-reviewed *and* well read. Most young ladies had some musical ability and singing was popular, either solo or in groups with piano accompaniment. Sheet music for such hits as "I Dreamt that I Dwelt in Marble Halls" and "The Last Rose of Summer" were best sellers, and many ladies' magazines published new music for piano or guitar along with their fashion news and serial stories. The same pianist might find herself providing music for an impromptu dance or concert. Whist, backgammon, and, late in the century, bridge were all played, and surprisingly sophisticated company might also find itself involved in spirited games of old nursery favorites such as dumbo crambo, the old family coach, blind man's bluff, or charades. Some neighborhoods or exceptionally ambitious house parties presented amateur theatricals, or, if time did not allow a full production, then short costume skits called *tableaux vivants* in which famous sayings or familiar poems were acted out.

September

Sunday 23

Monday 24

Tuesday 25

Wednesday 26

Thursday 27

Rosh Hashanah

Friday 28

Saturday 29

September - October

Sunday 30

Monday 1

Tuesday 2

Wednesday 3

Thursday 4

Friday 5

Yom Kippur

Saturday 6

The New Game of Croquet

October

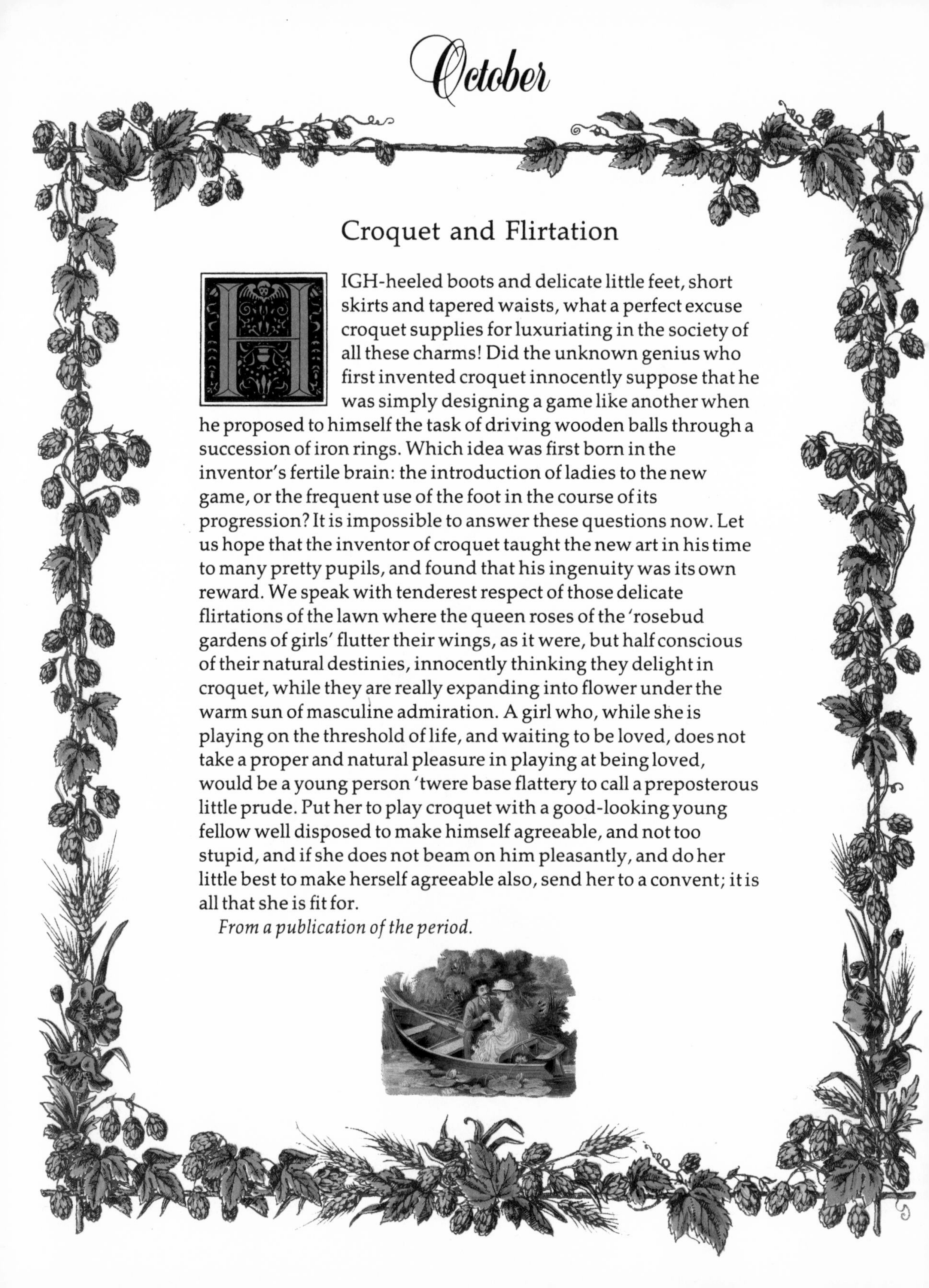

Croquet and Flirtation

HIGH-heeled boots and delicate little feet, short skirts and tapered waists, what a perfect excuse croquet supplies for luxuriating in the society of all these charms! Did the unknown genius who first invented croquet innocently suppose that he was simply designing a game like another when he proposed to himself the task of driving wooden balls through a succession of iron rings. Which idea was first born in the inventor's fertile brain: the introduction of ladies to the new game, or the frequent use of the foot in the course of its progression? It is impossible to answer these questions now. Let us hope that the inventor of croquet taught the new art in his time to many pretty pupils, and found that his ingenuity was its own reward. We speak with tenderest respect of those delicate flirtations of the lawn where the queen roses of the 'rosebud gardens of girls' flutter their wings, as it were, but half conscious of their natural destinies, innocently thinking they delight in croquet, while they are really expanding into flower under the warm sun of masculine admiration. A girl who, while she is playing on the threshold of life, and waiting to be loved, does not take a proper and natural pleasure in playing at being loved, would be a young person 'twere base flattery to call a preposterous little prude. Put her to play croquet with a good-looking young fellow well disposed to make himself agreeable, and not too stupid, and if she does not beam on him pleasantly, and do her little best to make herself agreeable also, send her to a convent; it is all that she is fit for.

From a publication of the period.

October

Sunday 7

Monday 8

Columbus Day 'Observed'

Tuesday 9

Wednesday 10

Thursday 11

Friday 12

Columbus Day

Saturday 13

October

Sunday 14

Monday 15

Tuesday 16

Wednesday 17

Thursday 18

Friday 19

Saturday 20

A Five O'Clock Tea

October

Time for Tea

MEANT to be a light meal to tide the diner over the lull between lunch and dinner, the Victorian tea expanded until the table could not hold another luscious muffin, scone, sandwich or cake. During the Season, tea time for Lady Margaret and her family is a time for receiving informal calls unless she has an afternoon engagement. She has a collection of wonderful tea gowns, those confections of embroidery and lace that allow the wearer to receive friends in flattering comfort. Her favorite is a stunning light wool gown by Worth in cream, shading to chestnut brown. Often the younger children come in to be shown off and introduced because Lady Margaret thinks it helps to develop their poise and social grace. Every two or three weeks she has a more formal "at home" tea, a large afternoon party at which there is professional entertainment, usually a singer or musician. Her friends take turns pouring at these events. In the country, tea is a little earlier. It is often the first time in the day the whole house party is gathered together. Sometimes her husband brings a neighbor in after a day's hunting, or other friends in the neighborhood pay calls. The tea table is more ample, too, to satisfy those who have been out-of-doors most of the day, and Lady Margaret makes sure that there are ham, beef, and chicken sandwiches as well as the more delicate watercress and cucumber. Madeira cake, fruit cake and Queen's cake, warm muffins and buttered toast, jam tarts and assorted biscuits as well as tea and "something stronger for the gentlemen" help to stave off the pangs of hunger until the gong sounds to dress for dinner.

October

Sunday 21

Monday 22

Tuesday 23

Wednesday 24

Thursday 25

Friday 26

Saturday 27

October - November

Sunday 28

Monday 29

Tuesday 30

Wednesday 31

Halloween

Thursday 1

Friday 2

Saturday 3

The Recital

November

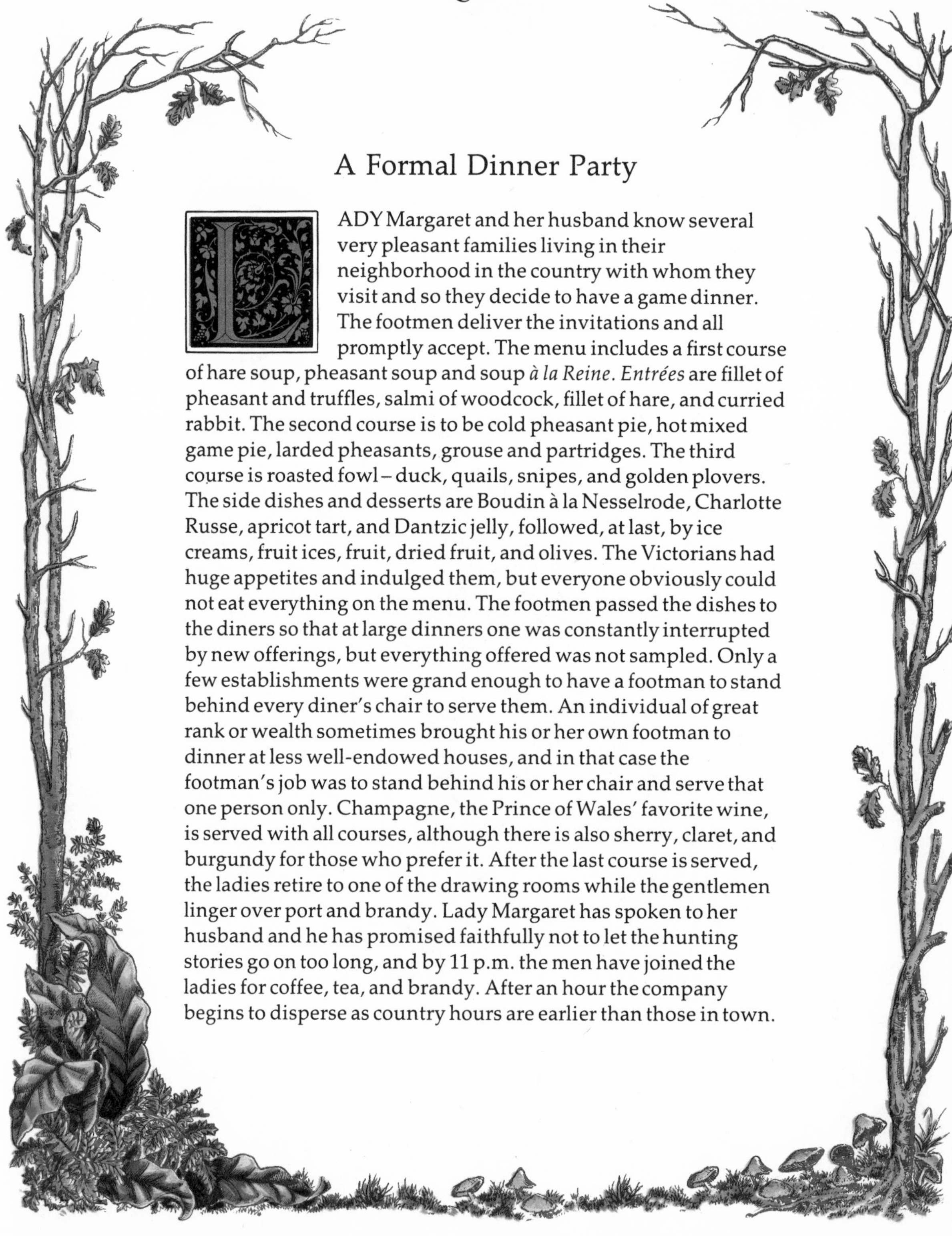

A Formal Dinner Party

LADY Margaret and her husband know several very pleasant families living in their neighborhood in the country with whom they visit and so they decide to have a game dinner. The footmen deliver the invitations and all promptly accept. The menu includes a first course of hare soup, pheasant soup and soup *à la Reine*. *Entrées* are fillet of pheasant and truffles, salmi of woodcock, fillet of hare, and curried rabbit. The second course is to be cold pheasant pie, hot mixed game pie, larded pheasants, grouse and partridges. The third course is roasted fowl – duck, quails, snipes, and golden plovers. The side dishes and desserts are Boudin à la Nesselrode, Charlotte Russe, apricot tart, and Dantzic jelly, followed, at last, by ice creams, fruit ices, fruit, dried fruit, and olives. The Victorians had huge appetites and indulged them, but everyone obviously could not eat everything on the menu. The footmen passed the dishes to the diners so that at large dinners one was constantly interrupted by new offerings, but everything offered was not sampled. Only a few establishments were grand enough to have a footman to stand behind every diner's chair to serve them. An individual of great rank or wealth sometimes brought his or her own footman to dinner at less well-endowed houses, and in that case the footman's job was to stand behind his or her chair and serve that one person only. Champagne, the Prince of Wales' favorite wine, is served with all courses, although there is also sherry, claret, and burgundy for those who prefer it. After the last course is served, the ladies retire to one of the drawing rooms while the gentlemen linger over port and brandy. Lady Margaret has spoken to her husband and he has promised faithfully not to let the hunting stories go on too long, and by 11 p.m. the men have joined the ladies for coffee, tea, and brandy. After an hour the company begins to disperse as country hours are earlier than those in town.

November

Sunday 4

Monday 5

Tuesday 6

Wednesday 7

Thursday 8

Friday 9

Saturday 10

November

Sunday 11

Veteran's Day

Monday 12

Tuesday 13

Wednesday 14

Thursday 15

Friday 16

Saturday 17

Preparing for the Ball

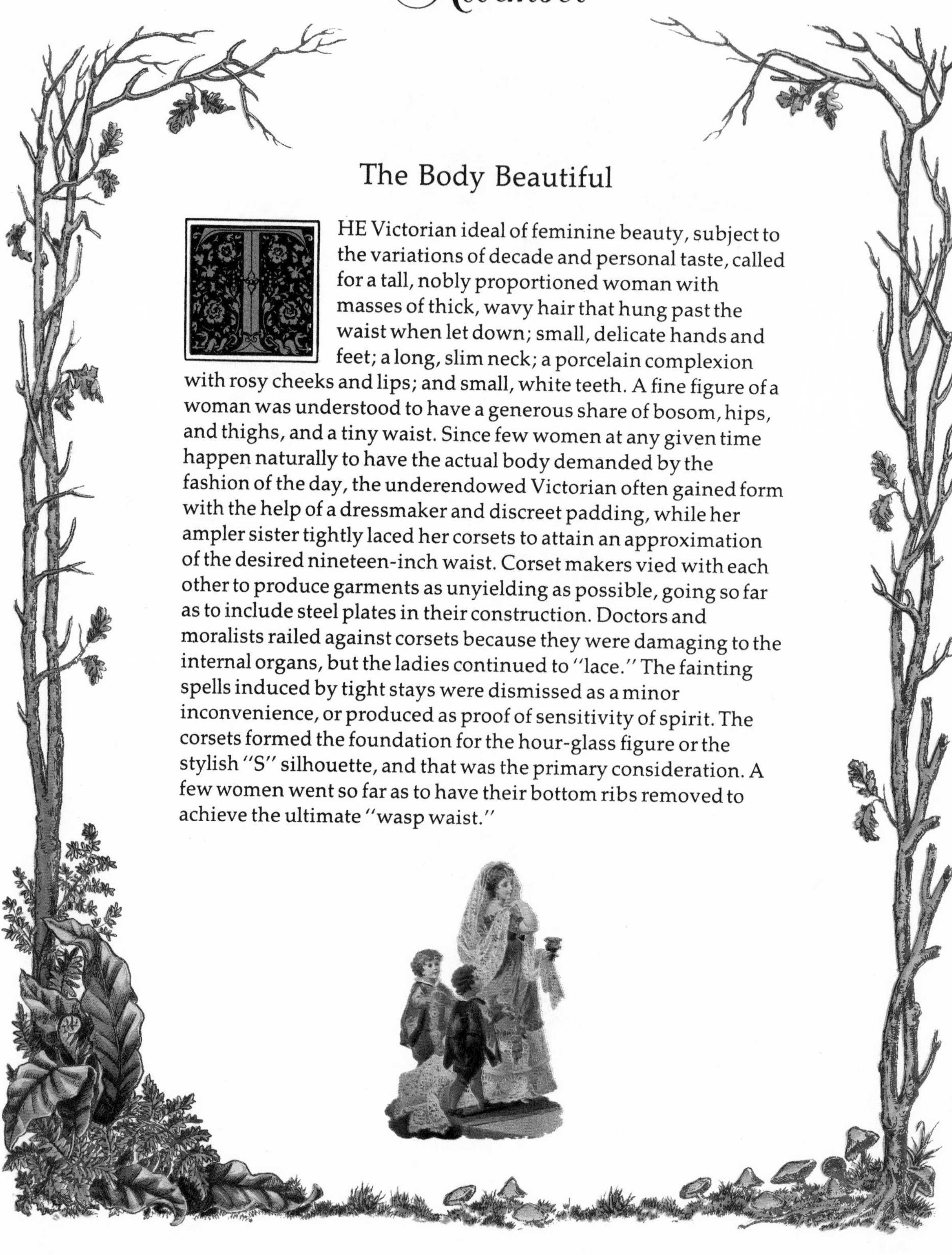

The Body Beautiful

THE Victorian ideal of feminine beauty, subject to the variations of decade and personal taste, called for a tall, nobly proportioned woman with masses of thick, wavy hair that hung past the waist when let down; small, delicate hands and feet; a long, slim neck; a porcelain complexion with rosy cheeks and lips; and small, white teeth. A fine figure of a woman was understood to have a generous share of bosom, hips, and thighs, and a tiny waist. Since few women at any given time happen naturally to have the actual body demanded by the fashion of the day, the underendowed Victorian often gained form with the help of a dressmaker and discreet padding, while her ampler sister tightly laced her corsets to attain an approximation of the desired nineteen-inch waist. Corset makers vied with each other to produce garments as unyielding as possible, going so far as to include steel plates in their construction. Doctors and moralists railed against corsets because they were damaging to the internal organs, but the ladies continued to "lace." The fainting spells induced by tight stays were dismissed as a minor inconvenience, or produced as proof of sensitivity of spirit. The corsets formed the foundation for the hour-glass figure or the stylish "S" silhouette, and that was the primary consideration. A few women went so far as to have their bottom ribs removed to achieve the ultimate "wasp waist."

November

Sunday 18

Monday 19

Tuesday 20

Wednesday 21

Thursday 22

Thanksgiving Day

Friday 23

Saturday 24

November-December

Sunday 25

Monday 26

Tuesday 27

Wednesday 28

Thursday 29

Friday 30

Saturday 1

The Ball

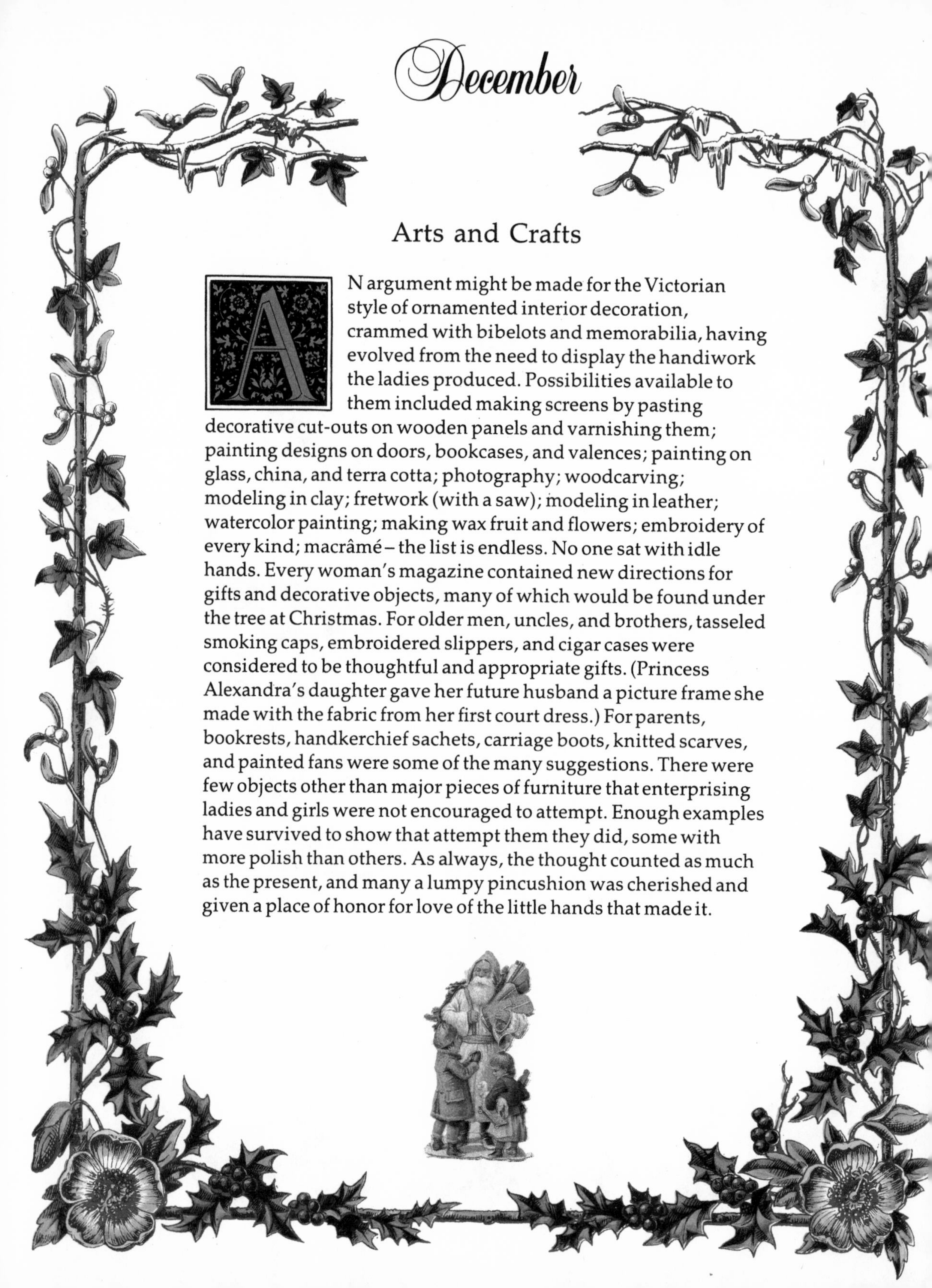

December

Arts and Crafts

AN argument might be made for the Victorian style of ornamented interior decoration, crammed with bibelots and memorabilia, having evolved from the need to display the handiwork the ladies produced. Possibilities available to them included making screens by pasting decorative cut-outs on wooden panels and varnishing them; painting designs on doors, bookcases, and valences; painting on glass, china, and terra cotta; photography; woodcarving; modeling in clay; fretwork (with a saw); modeling in leather; watercolor painting; making wax fruit and flowers; embroidery of every kind; macrâmé – the list is endless. No one sat with idle hands. Every woman's magazine contained new directions for gifts and decorative objects, many of which would be found under the tree at Christmas. For older men, uncles, and brothers, tasseled smoking caps, embroidered slippers, and cigar cases were considered to be thoughtful and appropriate gifts. (Princess Alexandra's daughter gave her future husband a picture frame she made with the fabric from her first court dress.) For parents, bookrests, handkerchief sachets, carriage boots, knitted scarves, and painted fans were some of the many suggestions. There were few objects other than major pieces of furniture that enterprising ladies and girls were not encouraged to attempt. Enough examples have survived to show that attempt them they did, some with more polish than others. As always, the thought counted as much as the present, and many a lumpy pincushion was cherished and given a place of honor for love of the little hands that made it.

December

Sunday 2

Monday 3

Tuesday 4

Wednesday 5

Thursday 6

Friday 7

Saturday 8

December

Sunday 9

Monday 10

Tuesday 11

Wednesday 12

Thursday 13

Friday 14

Saturday 15

The Christmas Party

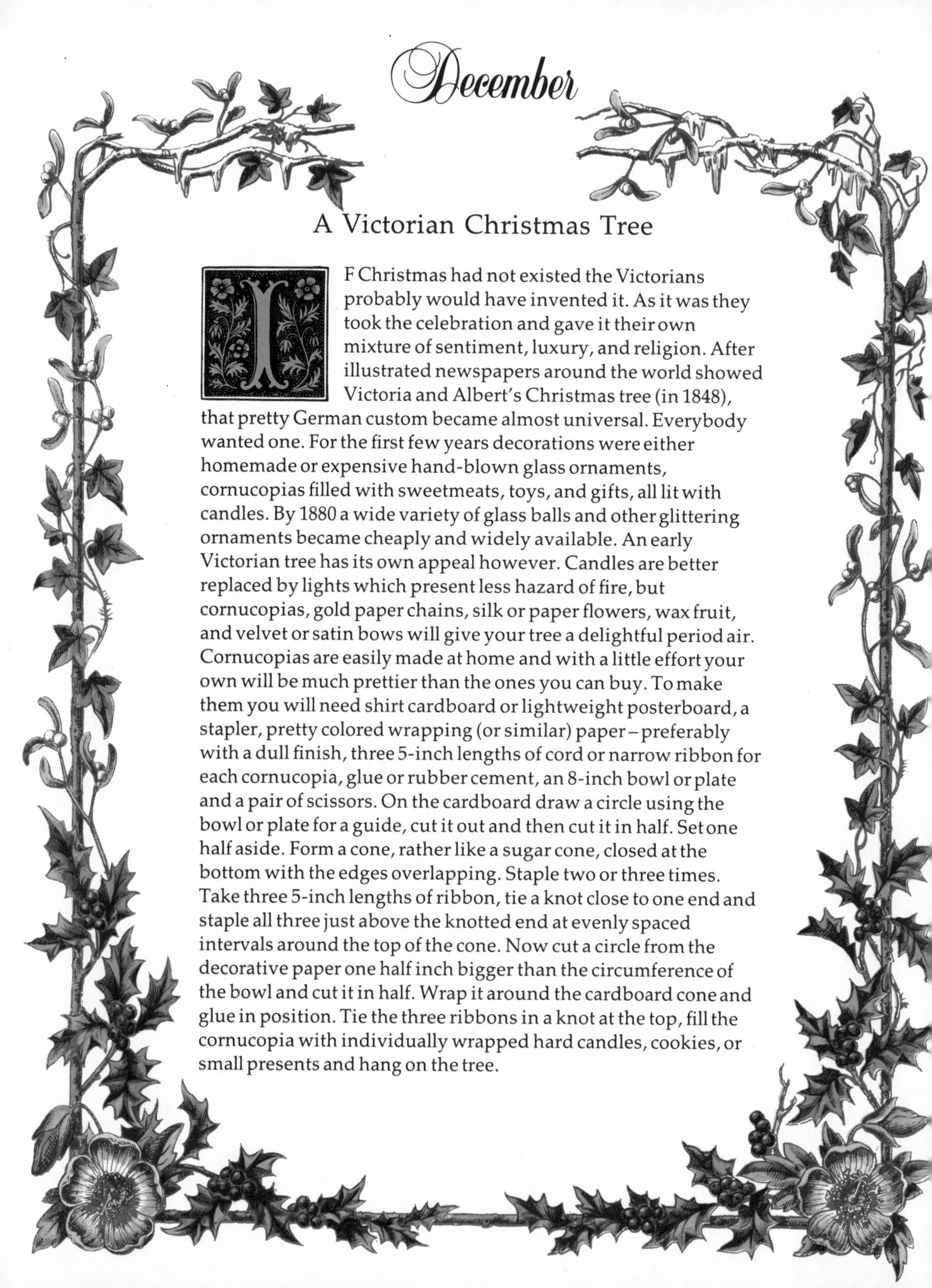

December

A Victorian Christmas Tree

IF Christmas had not existed the Victorians probably would have invented it. As it was they took the celebration and gave it their own mixture of sentiment, luxury, and religion. After illustrated newspapers around the world showed Victoria and Albert's Christmas tree (in 1848), that pretty German custom became almost universal. Everybody wanted one. For the first few years decorations were either homemade or expensive hand-blown glass ornaments, cornucopias filled with sweetmeats, toys, and gifts, all lit with candles. By 1880 a wide variety of glass balls and other glittering ornaments became cheaply and widely available. An early Victorian tree has its own appeal however. Candles are better replaced by lights which present less hazard of fire, but cornucopias, gold paper chains, silk or paper flowers, wax fruit, and velvet or satin bows will give your tree a delightful period air. Cornucopias are easily made at home and with a little effort your own will be much prettier than the ones you can buy. To make them you will need shirt cardboard or lightweight posterboard, a stapler, pretty colored wrapping (or similar) paper – preferably with a dull finish, three 5-inch lengths of cord or narrow ribbon for each cornucopia, glue or rubber cement, an 8-inch bowl or plate and a pair of scissors. On the cardboard draw a circle using the bowl or plate for a guide, cut it out and then cut it in half. Set one half aside. Form a cone, rather like a sugar cone, closed at the bottom with the edges overlapping. Staple two or three times. Take three 5-inch lengths of ribbon, tie a knot close to one end and staple all three just above the knotted end at evenly spaced intervals around the top of the cone. Now cut a circle from the decorative paper one half inch bigger than the circumference of the bowl and cut it in half. Wrap it around the cardboard cone and glue in position. Tie the three ribbons in a knot at the top, fill the cornucopia with individually wrapped hard candles, cookies, or small presents and hang on the tree.

December

Sunday 16

Monday 17

Tuesday 18

Wednesday 19

Hanukkah

Thursday 20

Friday 21

Saturday 22

December

Sunday 23

Monday 24

Tuesday 25

Christmas Day

Wednesday 26

Thursday 27

Friday 28

Saturday 29

The Christmas Tree

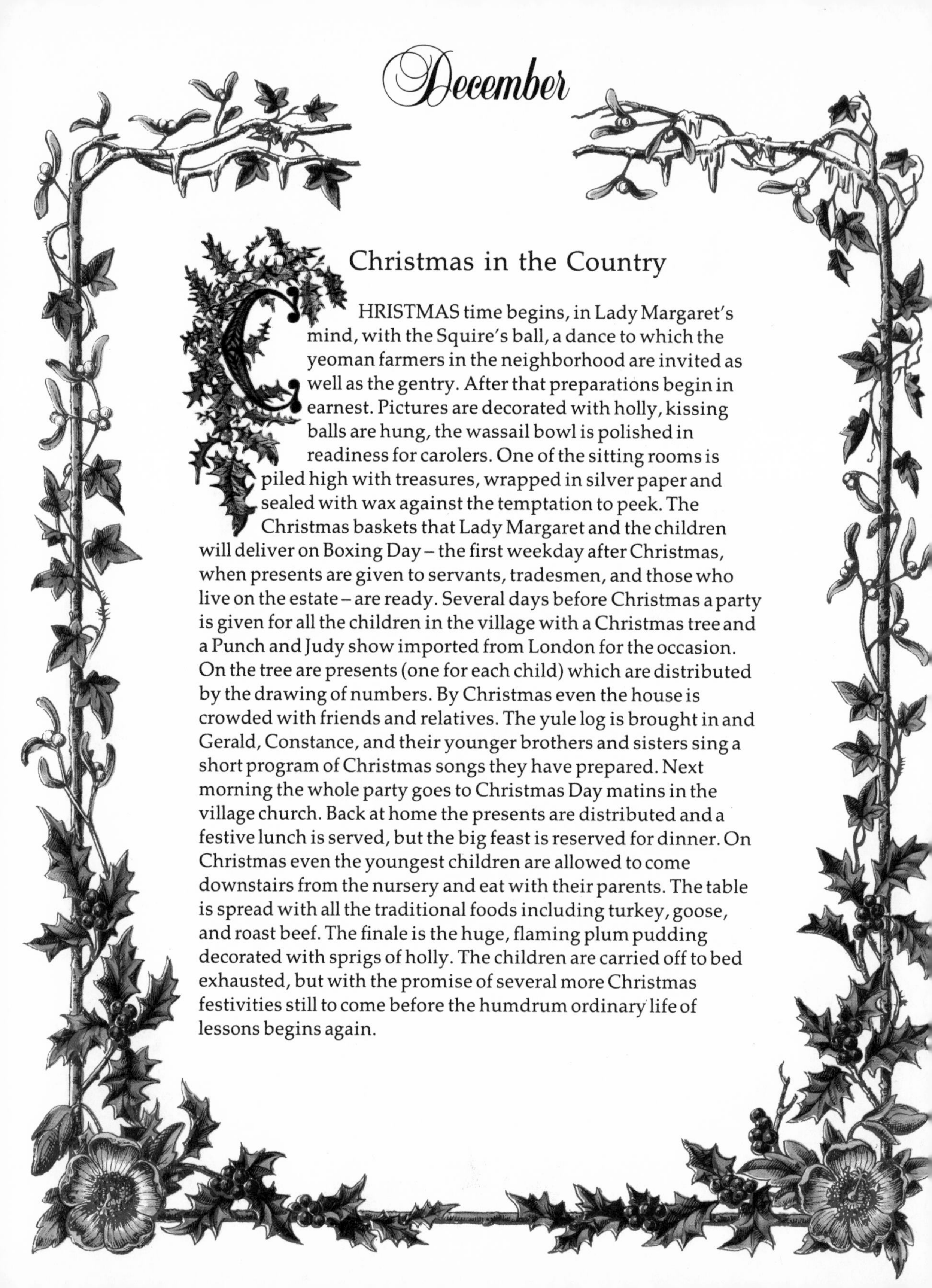

December

Christmas in the Country

CHRISTMAS time begins, in Lady Margaret's mind, with the Squire's ball, a dance to which the yeoman farmers in the neighborhood are invited as well as the gentry. After that preparations begin in earnest. Pictures are decorated with holly, kissing balls are hung, the wassail bowl is polished in readiness for carolers. One of the sitting rooms is piled high with treasures, wrapped in silver paper and sealed with wax against the temptation to peek. The Christmas baskets that Lady Margaret and the children will deliver on Boxing Day – the first weekday after Christmas, when presents are given to servants, tradesmen, and those who live on the estate – are ready. Several days before Christmas a party is given for all the children in the village with a Christmas tree and a Punch and Judy show imported from London for the occasion. On the tree are presents (one for each child) which are distributed by the drawing of numbers. By Christmas even the house is crowded with friends and relatives. The yule log is brought in and Gerald, Constance, and their younger brothers and sisters sing a short program of Christmas songs they have prepared. Next morning the whole party goes to Christmas Day matins in the village church. Back at home the presents are distributed and a festive lunch is served, but the big feast is reserved for dinner. On Christmas even the youngest children are allowed to come downstairs from the nursery and eat with their parents. The table is spread with all the traditional foods including turkey, goose, and roast beef. The finale is the huge, flaming plum pudding decorated with sprigs of holly. The children are carried off to bed exhausted, but with the promise of several more Christmas festivities still to come before the humdrum ordinary life of lessons begins again.

December-January

Sunday 30

Monday 31

Tuesday 1

New Year's Day

Wednesday 2

Thursday 3

Friday 4

Saturday 5

1984

JANUARY

M	T	W	T	F	S	S
						1
2	3	4	5	6	7	8
9	10	11	12	13	14	15
16	17	18	19	20	21	22
23	24	25	26	27	28	29
30	31					

FEBRUARY

M	T	W	T	F	S	S
		1	2	3	4	5
6	7	8	9	10	11	12
13	14	15	16	17	18	19
20	21	22	23	24	25	26
27	28	29				

MARCH

M	T	W	T	F	S	S
			1	2	3	4
5	6	7	8	9	10	11
12	13	14	15	16	17	18
19	20	21	22	23	24	25
26	27	28	29	30	31	

APRIL

M	T	W	T	F	S	S
						1
2	3	4	5	6	7	8
9	10	11	12	13	14	15
16	17	18	19	20	21	22
23	24	25	26	27	28	29
30						

MAY

M	T	W	T	F	S	S
	1	2	3	4	5	6
7	8	9	10	11	12	13
14	15	16	17	18	19	20
21	22	23	24	25	26	27
28	29	30	31			

JUNE

M	T	W	T	F	S	S
				1	2	3
4	5	6	7	8	9	10
11	12	13	14	15	16	17
18	19	20	21	22	23	24
25	26	27	28	29	30	

JULY

M	T	W	T	F	S	S
						1
2	3	4	5	6	7	8
9	10	11	12	13	14	15
16	17	18	19	20	21	22
23	24	25	26	27	28	29
30	31					

AUGUST

M	T	W	T	F	S	S
		1	2	3	4	5
6	7	8	9	10	11	12
13	14	15	16	17	18	19
20	21	22	23	24	25	26
27	28	29	30	31		

SEPTEMBER

M	T	W	T	F	S	S
					1	2
3	4	5	6	7	8	9
10	11	12	13	14	15	16
17	18	19	20	21	22	23
24	25	26	27	28	29	30

OCTOBER

M	T	W	T	F	S	S
1	2	3	4	5	6	7
8	9	10	11	12	13	14
15	16	17	18	19	20	21
22	23	24	25	26	27	28
29	30	31				

NOVEMBER

M	T	W	T	F	S	S
			1	2	3	4
5	6	7	8	9	10	11
12	13	14	15	16	17	18
19	20	21	22	23	24	25
26	27	28	29	30		

DECEMBER

M	T	W	T	F	S	S
					1	2
3	4	5	6	7	8	9
10	11	12	13	14	15	16
17	18	19	20	21	22	23
24	25	26	27	28	29	30
31						

1985

JANUARY

M	T	W	T	F	S	S
	1	2	3	4	5	6
7	8	9	10	11	12	13
14	15	16	17	18	19	20
21	22	23	24	25	26	27
28	29	30	31			

FEBRUARY

M	T	W	T	F	S	S
				1	2	3
4	5	6	7	8	9	10
11	12	13	14	15	16	17
18	19	20	21	22	23	24
25	26	27	28			

MARCH

M	T	W	T	F	S	S
				1	2	3
4	5	6	7	8	9	10
11	12	13	14	15	16	17
18	19	20	21	22	23	24
25	26	27	28	29	30	31

APRIL

M	T	W	T	F	S	S
1	2	3	4	5	6	7
8	9	10	11	12	13	14
15	16	17	18	19	20	21
22	23	24	25	26	27	28
29	30					

MAY

M	T	W	T	F	S	S
		1	2	3	4	5
6	7	8	9	10	11	12
13	14	15	16	17	18	19
20	21	22	23	24	25	26
27	28	29	30	31		

JUNE

M	T	W	T	F	S	S
					1	2
3	4	5	6	7	8	9
10	11	12	13	14	15	16
17	18	19	20	21	22	23
24	25	26	27	28	29	30

JULY

M	T	W	T	F	S	S
1	2	3	4	5	6	7
8	9	10	11	12	13	14
15	16	17	18	19	20	21
22	23	24	25	26	27	28
29	30	31				

AUGUST

M	T	W	T	F	S	S
			1	2	3	4
5	6	7	8	9	10	11
12	13	14	15	16	17	18
19	20	21	22	23	24	25
26	27	28	29	30	31	

SEPTEMBER

M	T	W	T	F	S	S
						1
2	3	4	5	6	7	8
9	10	11	12	13	14	15
16	17	18	19	20	21	22
23	24	25	26	27	28	29
30						

OCTOBER

M	T	W	T	F	S	S
	1	2	3	4	5	6
7	8	9	10	11	12	13
14	15	16	17	18	19	20
21	22	23	24	25	26	27
28	29	30	31			

NOVEMBER

M	T	W	T	F	S	S
				1	2	3
4	5	6	7	8	9	10
11	12	13	14	15	16	17
18	19	20	21	22	23	24
25	26	27	28	29	30	

DECEMBER

M	T	W	T	F	S	S
						1
2	3	4	5	6	7	8
9	10	11	12	13	14	15
16	17	18	19	20	21	22
23	24	25	26	27	28	29
30	31					

Telephone Numbers